Read me a Poem

Read me a Poem

Children's favorite poetry

Chosen by Ellen Lewis Buell

Former Editor of *The New York Times Book Review*

Illustrated by Anna Marie Magagna

ISBN: 0-448-02255-9

Library of Congress Catalog Card Number: 65-20043

© 1965, by Grosset & Dunlap, Inc.
GROSSET & DUNLAP · Publishers · NEW YORK
1974 PRINTING

The Whole Duty of a Poem

A poem should be, as our best ever are,
Golden of heart like a rose or a star.

A poem should be, like the brook that you hear
Sing down the mountainside, lovely and clear.

Yet in its music a poem should hold
That which is felt but may never be told.

Arthur Guiterman

How Many Miles to Babylon?

How many miles to Babylon?
Three score miles and ten.
Can I get there by candlelight?
Yes, and back again.

Traditional

Skyscrapers

Do skyscrapers ever grow tired
    Of holding themselves up high?
Do they ever shiver on frosty nights
    With their tops against the sky?
Do they feel lonely sometimes,
    Because they have grown so tall?
Do they ever wish they could lie right down
    And never get up at all?

Rachel Field

Mean Song

Snickles and podes,
Ribble and grodes:
That's what I wish you.

A nox in the groot,
A root in the stoot
And a gock in the forbeshaw, too.

Keep out of sight
For fear that I might
Glom you a gravely snave.

Don't show your face
Around any place
Or you'll get one flack snack in the bave.

Eve Merriam

8

A Prayer

From ghoulies and ghosties
And four-leggitty beasties
And things that go bump in the night
Good Lord, deliver us!

Traditional

When it comes to Bugs

I like crawlers,
I like creepers,
hoppers, jumpers,
fliers, leapers,
walkers, stalkers,
chirpers, peepers . . .

I wonder why
my Mother thinks
that finders can't be keepers?

Aileen Fisher

The Tickle Rhyme

"Who's that tickling my back?" said the wall.
"Me," said a small
Caterpillar. "I'm learning
To crawl."

Ian Serraillier

Bee Song

Bees in the late summer sun
Drone their song
Of yellow moons
Trimming black velvet,
Droning, droning a sleepysong.

Carl Sandburg

I'll tell you how the sun rose, —
A ribbon at a time.
The steeples swam in amethyst,
The news like squirrels ran.

The hills untied their bonnets,
The bobolinks begun.
Then I said softly to myself,
"That must have been the sun!"

.   .   .   .   .   .

But how he set, I know not.
There seemed a purple stile
Which little yellow boys and girls
Were climbing all the while

Till when they reached the other side,
A dominie in gray
Put gently up the evening bars,
And led the flock away.

Emily Dickinson

The Pasture

I'm going out to clean the pasture spring;
I'll only stop to rake the leaves away
(And wait to watch the water clear, I may):
I sha'n't be gone long. You come, too.

I'm going out to fetch the little calf
That's standing by the mother. It's so young
It totters when she licks it with her tongue.
I sha'n't be gone long. You come, too.

Robert Frost

The Morns

The morns are meeker than they were,
The nuts are getting brown;
The berry's cheek is plumper,
The rose is out of town.

The maple wears a gayer scarf,
The field a scarlet gown.
Lest I should be old-fashioned,
I'll put a trinket on.

Emily Dickinson

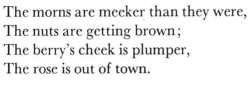

Winter Streams

Now the little rivers go
Muffled safely under snow,

And the winding meadow streams
Murmur in their wintry dreams,

While a tinkling music wells
Faintly from their icy bells

Telling how their hearts are bold,
Though the very sun be cold.

Ah, but wait until the rain
Comes a-sighing once again,

Sweeping softly from the Sound
Over ridge and meadow ground!

Then the little streams will hear
April calling far and near,

Slip their snowy bands and run
Sparkling in the welcome sun.

Bliss Carman

11

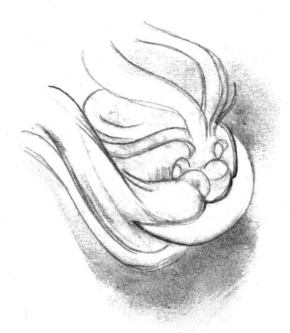

The Moon's the North Wind's Cooky

The Moon's the North Wind's cooky.
He bites it, day by day,
Until there's but a rim of scraps
That crumble all away.

The South Wind is a baker.
He kneads clouds in his den,
And bakes a crisp new moon *that . . . greedy*
North . . . Wind . . . eats . . . again!

Vachel Lindsay

Who Has Seen the Wind?

Who has seen the wind?
　　Neither I nor you:
But when the leaves hang trembling,
　　The wind is passing thro'.

Who has seen the wind?
　　Neither you nor I:
But when the trees bow down their heads,
　　The wind is passing by.

Christina Rossetti

From: Pippa Passes

The year's at the spring,
And day's at the morn;
Morning's at seven;
The hillside's dew-pearled;
The lark's on the wing;
The snail's on the thorn;
God's in His heaven —
All's right with the world!

Robert Browning

Windy Nights

Whenever the moon and stars are set,
    Whenever the wind is high,
All night long in the dark and wet,
    A man goes riding by.
Late in the night when the fires are out,
Why does he gallop and gallop about?

Whenever the trees are crying aloud,
    And ships are tossed at sea,
By, on the highway, low and loud,
    By at the gallop goes he;
By at the gallop he goes, and then
By he comes back at the gallop again.

Robert Louis Stevenson

In the Summer

In the summer, in the evenings,
When the day's been very warm,
Then we walk without our shoes on
In the long grass on the farm.

And the fireflies in the bushes
Prick the darkness all around,
And the crickets, very busy,
Make their nighttime summer sound.

And the grass is cold and dewy
After all the long day's heat,
But the steppingstones set in it
Still are warm beneath our feet.

Dorothy Aldis

13

Little Fox Lost

"It is dark in the world," wept the little fox,
"And I don't know where I am!
There are three big sheep in that uphill field
And a great big black-faced ram!"

"It is dark in the wood," said the little fox,
"And I've lost the starmoss way!
The trees are tall and my fur is wet —
What will my mother say?"

"My fur is wet with the starlit dew,
A cobweb tickles my nose,
And my heart is a grasshopper wild in my chest —
Where *am* I, do you suppose?"

"It is dark in the world!" sobbed the little fox.
"This path must be wrong! Here's another —"
"You're safe at my side!   You're right at the door!
Big foxes don't cry!" said his mother.

Frances Frost

14

Sea Fever

I must go down to the seas again, to the lonely sea and the sky,
And all I ask is a tall ship and a star to steer her by,
And the wheel's kick and the wind's song and the white sail's shaking,
And a grey mist on the sea's face and a grey dawn breaking.

I must go down to the seas again, for the call of the running tide
Is a wild call and a clear call that may not be denied;
And all I ask is a windy day with the white clouds flying,
And the flung spray and the blown spume, and the sea-gulls crying.

I must go down to the seas again, to the vagrant gypsy life,
To the gull's way and the whale's way where the wind's like
    a whetted knife;
And all I ask is a merry yarn from a laughing fellow-rover,
And quiet sleep and a sweet dream when the long trick's over.

John Masefield

What is Pink?

What is pink? a rose is pink
By the fountain's brink.
What is red? a poppy's red
In its barley bed.
What is blue? the sky is blue
Where the clouds float thro'.
What is white? a swan is white
Sailing in the light.
What is yellow? pears are yellow,
Rich and ripe and mellow.
What is green? the grass is green,
With small flowers between.
What is violet? clouds are violet
In the summer twilight.
What is orange? why, an orange,
Just an orange!

Christina Rossetti

A Vagabond Song

There is something in the autumn that is native to my blood —
Touch of manner, hint of mood;
And my heart is like a rhyme,
With the yellow and the purple and the crimson keeping time.

The scarlet of the maples can shake me like a cry
Of bugles going by.
And my lonely spirit thrills
To see the frosty asters like a smoke upon the hills.

There is something in October sets the gypsy blood astir;
We must rise and follow her,
When from every hill of flame
She calls and calls each vagabond by name.

Bliss Carman

From: The Bells

Hear the sledges with the bells —
    Silver bells!
What a world of merriment their melody foretells!
    How they tinkle, tinkle, tinkle,
        In the icy air of night!
    While the stars, that oversprinkle
    All the heavens, seem to twinkle
        With a crystalline delight;
    Keeping time, time, time,
    In a sort of Runic rhyme,
To the tintinnabulation that so musically wells
    From the bells, bells, bells, bells,
        Bells, bells, bells —
    From the jingling and the tinkling of the bells.

Edgar Allan Poe

Ariel's Songs

Come unto these yellow sands,
    And then take hands:
Court'sied when you have, and kiss'd
    (The wild waves whist,)
Foot it featly here and there;
And, sweet sprites, the burden bear.

Where the bee sucks, there suck I:
In a cowslip's bell I lie;
There I couch when owls do cry.
On the bat's back I do fly
After summer, merrily:
Merrily, merrily, shall I live now,
Under the blossom that hangs on the bough.

William Shakespeare

The Fairies

Up the airy mountain,
    Down the rushy glen,
We daren't go a-hunting
    For fear of little men;
Wee folk, good folk,
    Trooping all together;
Green jacket, red cap,
    And white owl's feather.

Down along the rocky shore
    Some make their home,
They live on crispy pancakes
    Of yellow tide-foam;
Some in the reeds
    Of the black mountain lake,
With frogs for their watchdogs,
    All night awake.

High on the hilltop
    The old King sits;
He is now so old and gray
    He's nigh lost his wits.
With a bridge of white mist
    Columbkill he crosses,
On his stately journeys
    From Slieveleague to Rosses;
Or going up with music
    On cold starry nights,
To sup with the Queen
    Of the gay Northern Lights.

They stole little Bridget
    For seven years long;
When she came down again
    Her friends were all gone.
They took her lightly back,
    Between the night and morrow,
They thought that she was fast asleep,
    But she was dead with sorrow.
They have kept her ever since
    Deep within the lake,
On a bed of flag-leaves,
    Watching till she wake.

By the craggy hillside,
    Through the mosses bare,
They have planted thorn-trees
    For pleasure here and there.
Is any man so daring
    As dig them up in spite,
He shall find their sharpest thorns
    In his bed at night.

Up the airy mountain,
    Down the rushy glen,
We daren't go a-hunting
    For fear of little men;
Wee folk, good folk,
    Trooping all together;
Green jacket, red cap,
    And white owl's feather!

William Allingham

The Eagle

He clasps the crag with crooked hands;
Close to the sun in lonely lands,
Ringed with the azure world, he stands.

The wrinkled sea beneath him crawls;
He watches from his mountain walls,
And like a thunderbolt he falls.

Alfred, Lord Tennyson

Seal Lullaby

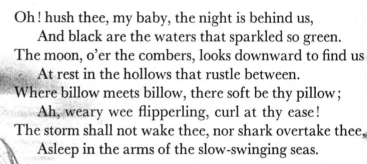

Oh! hush thee, my baby, the night is behind us,
    And black are the waters that sparkled so green.
The moon, o'er the combers, looks downward to find us
    At rest in the hollows that rustle between.
Where billow meets billow, there soft be thy pillow;
    Ah, weary wee flipperling, curl at thy ease!
The storm shall not wake thee, nor shark overtake thee,
    Asleep in the arms of the slow-swinging seas.

Rudyard Kipling

From: Where Are You Now?

When the night begins to fall
And the sky begins to glow
You look up and see the tall
City of light begin to grow —
In rows and little golden squares
The lights come out. First here, then there
Behind the windowpanes as though
A million billion bees had built
Their golden hives and honeycombs
Above you in the air.

Mary Britton Miller

Japanese Lullaby

Sleep, little pigeon, and fold your wings —
    Little blue pigeon with velvet eyes;
Sleep to the singing of mother-bird swinging —
    Swinging the nest where her little one lies.

Away out yonder I see a star —
    Silvery star with a tinkling song;
To the soft dew falling I hear it calling —
    Calling and tinkling the night along.

In through the window a moonbeam comes —
    Little gold moonbeam with misty wings;
All silently creeping, it asks: "Is he sleeping —
    Sleeping and dreaming while mother sings?"

Up from the sea there floats a sob
    Of the waves that are breaking upon the shore,
As though they were groaning in anguish, and moaning —
    Bemoaning the ship that shall come no more.

But sleep, little pigeon, and fold your wings —
    Little blue pigeon with mournful eyes;
Am I not singing? — see, I am swinging —
    Swinging the nest where my darling lies.

Eugene Field

Building

The first thing we did
Was pound out straight
Some nails, then we found
A carton and crate

And nailed them on top
Of a pretty big box,
And we all had hammers
Of smoothish rocks,

And how can you build things
Without some noise,
But it seems to bother
The sisters of boys.

Harry Behn

Song of the Train

Clickety-clack,
Wheels on the track,
This is the way
They begin the attack:
Click-ety-clack,
Click-ety-clack,
Click-ety, *clack*-ety,
Click-ety
Clack.

Clickety-clack,
Over the crack,
Faster and faster
The song of the track:
Clickety-clack,
Clickety-clack,
Clickety, clackety,
Clackety
Clack.

David McCord

This is the Key

This is the Key of the Kingdom
In that Kingdom is a city;
In that city is a town;
In that town there is a street;
In that street there winds a lane;
In that lane there is a yard;
In that yard there is a house;
In that house there waits a room;
In that room an empty bed;
And on that bed a basket —
A Basket of Sweet Flowers:
   Of Flowers, of Flowers;
   A Basket of Sweet Flowers.

Flowers in a Basket;
Basket on the bed;
Bed in the chamber;
Chamber in the house;
House in the weedy yard;
Yard in the winding lane;
Lane in the broad street;
Street in the high town;
Town in the city;
City in the Kingdom —
This is the Key of the Kingdom.
   Of the Kingdom this is the Key.

Unknown

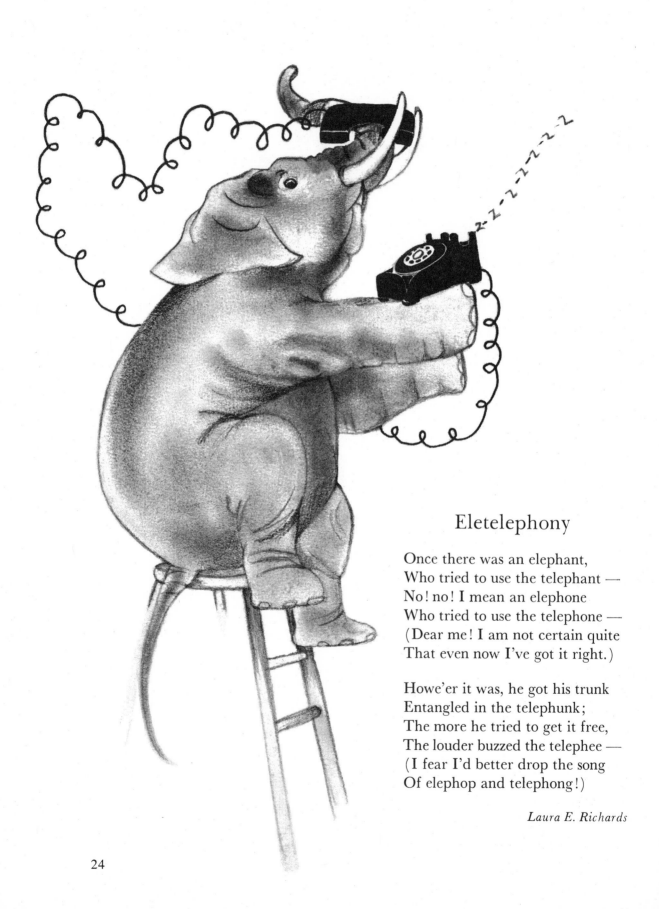

Eletelephony

Once there was an elephant,
Who tried to use the telephant —
No! no! I mean an elephone
Who tried to use the telephone —
(Dear me! I am not certain quite
That even now I've got it right.)

Howe'er it was, he got his trunk
Entangled in the telephunk;
The more he tried to get it free,
The louder buzzed the telephee —
(I fear I'd better drop the song
Of elephop and telephong!)

Laura E. Richards

24

The Lost Doll

I once had a sweet little doll, dears,
    The prettiest doll in the world;
Her cheeks were so red and white, dears,
    And her hair was so charmingly curled.
But I lost my poor little doll, dears,
    As I played on the heath one day;
And I cried for her more than a week, dears,
    But I never could find where she lay.

I found my poor little doll, dears,
    As I played on the heath one day;
Folks say she is terribly changed, dears,
    For her paint is all washed away,
And her arms trodden off by the cows, dears,
    And her hair not the least bit curled;
Yet for old sake's sake, she is still, dears,
    The prettiest doll in the world.

Charles Kingsley

I Remember

I remember, I remember,
The house where I was born,
The little window where the sun
Came peeping in at morn;
He never came a wink too soon,
Nor brought too long a day;
But now, I often wish the night
Had borne my breath away.

I remember, I remember,
The roses, red and white,
The violets, and the lily-cups!
Those flowers made of light!
The lilacs where the robin built,
And where my brother set
The laburnum on his birthday,
The tree is living yet!

I remember, I remember,
Where I used to swing,
And thought the air must rush as fresh
To swallows on the wing;
My spirit flew in feathers then,
That is so heavy now,
And summer pools could hardly cool
The fever on my brow!

I remember, I remember,
The fir trees dark and high;
I used to think their slender tops
Were close against the sky:
It was a childish ignorance,
But now 'tis little joy
To know I'm farther off from Heaven
Than when I was a boy.

Thomas Hood

26

From: My Lost Youth

Often I think of the beautiful town
    That is seated by the sea;
Often in thought go up and down
The pleasant streets of that dear old town,
    And my youth comes back to me.
        And a verse of Lapland song
        Is haunting my memory still:
           "A boy's will is the wind's will,
And the thoughts of youth are long, long thoughts."

                I can see the shadowy lines of its trees,
                    And catch in sudden gleams,
                The sheen of the far-surrounding seas,
                And islands that were the Hesperides
                    Of all my boyish dreams.
                        And the burden of that old song,
                        It murmurs and whispers still:
                            "A boy's will is the wind's will,
            And the thoughts of youth are long, long thoughts."

I remember the black wharves and the slips,
    And the sea-tides tossing free;
And Spanish sailors with bearded lips,
And the beauty and mystery of the ships,
    And the magic of the sea.
        And the voice of that wayward song
        Is singing and saying still:
           "A boy's will is the wind's will,
And the thoughts of youth are long, long thoughts."

       Henry Wadsworth Longfellow

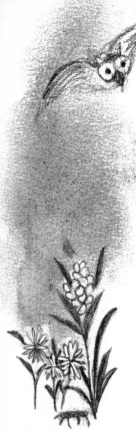

Some One

Some one came knocking
    At my wee, small door;
Some one came knocking,
    I'm sure — sure — sure;
I listened, I opened,
    I looked to left and right,
But nought there was a-stirring
    In the still dark night;
Only the busy beetle
    Tap-tapping in the wall,
Only from the forest
    The screech-owl's call,
Only the cricket whistling
    While the dewdrops fall,
So I know not who came knocking,
    At all, at all, at all.

Walter de la Mare

The Reason for the Pelican

The reason for the pelican
Is difficult to see:
His beak is clearly larger
Than there's any need to be.

It's not to bail a boat with —
He doesn't own a boat.
Yet everywhere he takes himself
He has that beak to tote.

It's not to keep his wife in —
His wife has got one, too.
It's not a scoop for eating soup.
It's not an extra shoe.

It isn't quite for anything.
And yet you realize
It's really quite a splendid beak
In quite a splendid size.

John Ciardi

Songs of Seven

SEVEN TIMES ONE.   EXULTATION.

There's no dew left on the daisies and clover,
  There's no rain left in heaven:
I've said my "seven times" over and over,
  Seven times one are seven.

I am old, so old, I can write a letter;
  My birthday lessons are done;
The lambs play always, they know no better;
  They are only one times one.

O moon! in the night I have seen you sailing
  And shining so round and low;
You were bright! ah bright! but your light is failing —
  You are nothing now but a bow.

You moon, have you done something wrong in heaven
  That God has hidden your face?
I hope if you have you will soon be forgiven,
  And shine again in your place.

O velvet bee, you're a dusty fellow,
  You've powdered your legs with gold!
O brave marsh marybuds, rich and yellow,
  Give me your money to hold!

O columbine, open your folded wrapper
  Where two twin turtle-doves dwell!
O cuckoo pint, toll me the purple clapper
  That hangs in your clear green bell!

And show me your nest with the young ones in it;
  I will not steal them away;
I am old! you may trust me, linnet, linnet —
  I am seven times one today.

Jean Ingelow

The Modern Hiawatha

He killed the noble Mudjokivis;
With the skin he made him mittens,
Made them with the fur side inside,
Made them with the skin side outside,
He, to get the warm side inside,
Put the inside skin side outside:
He, to get the cold side outside,
Put the warm side fur side inside:
That's why he put the fur side inside,
Why he put the skin side outside,
Why he turned them inside outside.

George A. Strong

Ducks' Ditty

All along the backwater,
Through the rushes tall,
Ducks are a-dabbling,
Up tails all!

Ducks' tails, drakes' tails,
Yellow feet a-quiver,
Yellow bills all out of sight
Busy in the river!

Slushy green undergrowth
Where the roach swim —
Here we keep our larder,
Cool and full and dim.

Everyone for what he likes!
We like to be
Heads down, tails up,
Dabbling free!

High in the blue above
Swifts whirl and call —
We are down a-dabbling
Up tails all!

Kenneth Grahame

A Tragic Story

There lived a sage in days of yore,
And he a handsome pigtail wore;
But wondered much, and sorrowed more,
    Because it hung behind him.

He mused upon this curious case,
And swore he'd change the pigtail's place,
And have it hanging at his face,
    Not dangling there behind him.

Says he, "The mystery I've found, —
I'll turn me round," — he turned him round,
    But still it hung behind him.

Then round and round, and out and in,
All day the puzzled sage did spin;
In vain — it mattered not a pin —
    The pigtail hung behind him.

And right and left, and round about,
And up and down and in and out
He turned; but still the pigtail stout
    Hung steadily behind him.

And though his efforts never slack,
And though he twist, and twirl, and tack,
Alas! still faithful to his back,
    The pigtail hangs behind him.

William Makepeace Thackeray

31

Hallowe'en

Tonight is the night
When dead leaves fly
Like witches on switches
Across the sky,
When elf and sprite
Flit through the night
On a moony sheen.

Tonight is the night
When leaves make a sound
Like a gnome in his home
Under the ground,
When spooks and trolls
Creep out of holes
Mossy and green.

Tonight is the night
When pumpkins stare
Through sheaves and leaves
Everywhere,
When ghoul and ghost
And goblin host
Dance round their queen.
It's Hallowe'en.

Harry Behn.

The Owl

When cats run home and light is come,
  And dew is cold upon the ground,
And the far-off stream is dumb,
  And the whirring sail goes round,
  And the whirring sail goes round;
    Alone and warming his five wits,
    The white owl in the belfry sits.

When merry milkmaids click the latch,
  And rarely smells the new-mown hay,
And the cock hath sung beneath the thatch
  Twice or thrice his roundelay,
  Twice or thrice his roundelay;
    Alone and warming his five wits,
    The white owl in the belfry sits.

Alfred Tennyson

The Tiger

Tiger! Tiger! burning bright
In the forests of the night,
What immortal hand or eye
Could frame thy fearful symmetry?

In what distant deeps or skies
Burnt the fire of thine eyes?
On what wings dare he aspire?
What the hand dare seize the fire?

And what shoulder, and what art,
Could twist the sinews of thy heart?
And when thy heart began to beat,
What dread hand? and what dread feet?

What the hammer? what the chain?
In what furnace was thy brain?
What the anvil? what dread grasp
Dare its deadly terrors clasp?

When the stars threw down their spears,
And watered heaven with their tears,
Did he smile his work to see?
Did he who made the Lamb make thee?

Tiger! Tiger! burning bright
In the forests of the night,
What immortal hand or eye,
Dare frame thy fearful symmetry?

William Blake

From: The Rhyme of the Ancient Mariner

He prayeth best, who loveth best
All things both great and small;
For the dear God who loveth us,
He made and loveth all.

Samuel Taylor Coleridge

Fairy's Song

Over hill, over dale,
    Through bush, through brier,
Over park, over pale,
    Through flood, through fire,
I do wander everywhere,
Swifter than the moon's sphere;
And I serve the fairy queen:
To dew her orbs upon the green:
The cowslips tall her pensioners be;
In their gold coats spots you see;
Those be rubies, fairy favours,
In those freckles live their savours:
I must go seek some dewdrops here,
And hang a pearl in every cowslip's ear.

William Shakespeare

White Magic

When tree-toads trill and crickets chirr
    And all the marshlands faintly ring,
A goblin flits through plumes of fir
    Upon the wood-owl's velvet wing;

He fills with fern-seed, brown and dry,
    His acorn pipe; when winds are whist
He lights it with a firefly —
    And hillward blows the evening mist.

Arthur Guiterman

Under the Greenwood Tree

Under the greenwood tree
Who loves to lie with me,
And turn his merry note
Unto the sweet bird's throat.
Come hither, come hither, come hither:
Here shall he see
No enemy,
But winter and rough weather.

William Shakespeare

Daffadowndilly

Growing in the vale
By the uplands hilly,
Growing straight and frail,
Lady Daffadowndilly.

In a golden crown,
And a scant green gown
While the spring blows chilly,
Lady Daffadown,
Sweet Daffadowndilly.

Christina Rossetti

Firefly Song

Firefly in the pool of water,
Bring me up a little silver,
Bring me up a star for the delight of it,
Bring me up a broken moon.

Firefly, firefly, in the water,
Bring me up a golden river,
Bring me up a fish with a light on it,
Bring me up a crooked moon.

Elizabeth Madox Roberts

THE VIKING PRESS, INC. — "Firefly Song,"
from *Under the Tree*, by Elizabeth Madox
Roberts, copyright 1922 by B. W. Huebsch,
Inc., 1950 by Ivor S. Roberts. Reprinted by
permission of The Viking Press, Inc.

What is Brown?

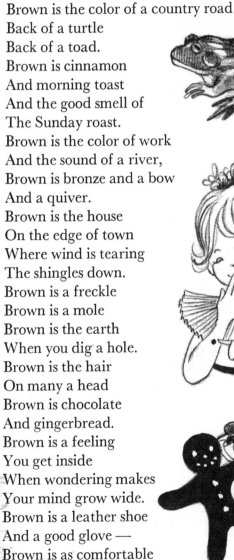

Brown is the color of a country road
Back of a turtle
Back of a toad.
Brown is cinnamon
And morning toast
And the good smell of
The Sunday roast.
Brown is the color of work
And the sound of a river,
Brown is bronze and a bow
And a quiver.
Brown is the house
On the edge of town
Where wind is tearing
The shingles down.
Brown is a freckle
Brown is a mole
Brown is the earth
When you dig a hole.
Brown is the hair
On many a head
Brown is chocolate
And gingerbread.
Brown is a feeling
You get inside
When wondering makes
Your mind grow wide.
Brown is a leather shoe
And a good glove —
Brown is as comfortable
As love.

Mary O'Neill

The Golden Rod

Spring is the morning of the year,
    And summer is the noontide bright;
The autumn is the evening clear
    That comes before the winter's night.

And in the evening, everywhere
    Along the roadside, up and down,
I see the golden torches flare
    Like lighted street-lamps in the town.

I think the butterfly and bee,
    From distant meadows coming back,
Are quite contented when they see
    These lamps along the homeward track.

But those who stay too late get lost;
    For when the darkness falls about,
Down every lighted street the Frost
    Will go and put the torches out!

Frank Dempster Sherman

38

Christmas Eve Legend

The woods were still and the snow was deep,
But there was no creature who could sleep.

The fox and the vixen ran together
Silently through the starry weather.

The buck and the doe and the fawn came drifting
Into the clearing. The rabbit, lifting

His ears, shook white from the twigs he brushed;
The chattering squirrel for once was hushed

As he sat with his paws against his breast,
And the bobcat crouched on the mountain crest.

Safe in the fold the silver sheep
Told the young lambs not to leap.

In the shadowy stable the horses stood
Hearing the quietness in the wood,

And the cattle sighed in the fragrant barn,
Waiting the instant of the morn.

The stars stood at midnight, and tame or wild,
All creatures knelt to worship the Child.

Frances Frost

Daisy's Song

1.

The sun, with his great eye,
Sees not so much as I;
And the moon, all silver-proud,
Might as well be in a cloud.

2.

And O the spring — the spring!
I lead the life of a king!
Couch'd in the teeming grass,
I spy each pretty lass.

3.

I look where no one dares,
And I stare where no one stares,
And, when the night is nigh,
Lambs bleat my lullaby.

John Keats

The Happy Hedgehog

The happiness of hedgehogs
   Lies in complete repose.
They spend the months of winter
   In a long delicious doze;
And if they note the time at all,
   They think "How fast it goes!"

E. V. Rieu

September

The goldenrod is yellow;
    The corn is turning brown;
The trees in apple orchards
    With fruit are bending down;

The gentian's bluest fringes
    Are curling in the sun;
In dusty pods the milkweed
    Its hidden silk has spun;

The sedges flaunt their harvest
    In every meadow nook,
And asters by the brookside
    Make asters in the brook.

From dewy lanes at morning
    The grapes' sweet odors rise;
At noon the roads all flutter
    With yellow butterflies —

By all these lovely tokens
    September days are here,
With summer's best of weather
    And autumn's best of cheer.

Helen Hunt Jackson

White Fields

1.

In the wintertime we go
Walking in the fields of snow;

Where there is no grass at all;
Where the top of every wall,

Every fence and every tree,
Is as white as white can be.

2.

Pointing out the way we came,
Everyone of them the same —

All across the fields there be
Prints in silver filigree;

And our mothers always know,
By our footprints in the snow,

Where the children go.

James Stephens

Motto for a Dog House

I love this little house because
    It offers, after dark,
A pause for rest, a rest for paws,
    A place to moor my bark.

Arthur Guiterman

Blow the Stars Home

Blow the Stars home, Wind, blow the Stars home
Ere Morning drowns them in golden foam.

Eleanor Farjeon

Requiem

Under the wide and starry sky,
Dig the grave and let me lie.
Glad did I live and gladly die,
　　And I laid me down with a will.

This be the verse you grave for me:
Here he lies where he longed to be;
Home is the sailor, home from sea,
　　And the hunter home from the hill.

Robert Louis Stevenson

I Never Saw a Moor

I never saw a moor,
I never saw the sea;
Yet know I how the heather looks,
And what a wave must be.

I never spoke with God,
Nor visited in heaven;
Yet certain am I of the spot
As if the chart were given.

Emily Dickinson

For My Grandmother

This lovely flower fell to seed;
Work gently sun and rain;
She held it as her dying creed
That she would grow again.

Countee Cullen

The Lobster Quadrille

"Will you walk a little faster?" said a whiting to a snail,
"There's a porpoise close behind us, and he's treading on my tail.
See how eagerly the lobsters and the turtles all advance!
They are waiting on the shingle — will you come and join the dance?
     Will you, won't you, will you, won't you, will you join the dance?
     Will you, won't you, will you, won't you, won't you join the dance?

"You can really have no notion how delightful it will be
When they take us up and throw us, with the lobsters, out to sea!"
But the snail replied, "Too far, too far!" and gave a look askance —
Said he thanked the whiting kindly, but he would not join the dance.
     Would not, could not, would not, could not, would not join the dance.
     Would not, could not, would not, could not, could not join the dance.

"What matters it how far we go?" his scaly friend replied.
"There is another shore, you know, upon the other side.
The further off from England, the nearer is to France —
Then turn not pale, beloved snail, but come and join the dance.
     Will you, won't you, will you, won't you, will you join the dance?
     Will you, won't you, will you, won't you, won't you join the dance?

Lewis Carroll

ACKNOWLEDGMENTS

Grateful acknowledgment is made to the following publishers, authors and copyright holders for permission to reprint material contained in this book:

ABELARD-SCHUMAN LIMITED — "When it Comes to Bugs," from *I Wonder How, I Wonder Why* by Aileen Fisher, copyright © 1962 by Abelard-Schuman Limited, reprinted by permission of the publishers.

ATHENEUM — "Mean Song," from *There is No Rhyme for Silver* by Eve Merriam, copyright 1962 by Eve Merriam, reprinted by permission of the publishers.

DODD, MEAD & COMPANY, INC. — "A Vagabond Song" and "Winter Streams," from *Bliss Carman's Poems*, reprinted by permission of Dodd, Mead & Co., Inc., copyright 1929 by Bliss Carman.

DOUBLEDAY & COMPANY, INC. — "What is Brown?" from *Hailstones and Halibut Bones* by Mary O'Neill, copyright © 1961 by Mary Gibbons O'Neill, reprinted by permission of Doubleday & Co., Inc.; "Seal Lullaby," from *The Jungle Book* by Rudyard Kipling. Reprinted by permission of Mrs. George Bambridge and Doubleday & Co., Inc.

E. P. DUTTON & COMPANY, INC. — "The Whole Duty of a Poem," and "Motto for a Dog House," from *Lyric Laughter* by Arthur Guiterman, copyright 1939 by E. P. Dutton & Co., Inc.; "White Magic," from *Death and General Putnam and 101 Other Poems* by Arthur Guiterman, copyright 1935 by E. P. Dutton & Co., Inc., renewal © 1963 by Mrs. Vida Lindo Guiterman; "The Happy Hedgehog," from *The Flattered Flying Fish and Other Poems* by E. V. Rieu, copyright © 1962 by E. V. Rieu. Reprinted by permission of E. P. Dutton & Co., Inc.

HARCOURT, BRACE & WORLD, INCORPORATED — "Building," from *Windy Morning* by Harry Behn, copyright 1953, by Harry Behn; "Hallowe'en," from *The Little Hill* by Harry Behn, copyright 1949 by Harry Behn; "Bee Song," from *Wind Song* by Carl Sandburg, copyright © 1960 by Carl Sandburg. Reprinted by permission of Harcourt, Brace & World, Incorporated.

HARPER & ROW, PUBLISHERS, INCORPORATED — "For My Grandmother," from *On These I Stand* by Countee Cullen, copyright 1925 by Harper & Brothers, renewed 1953 by Ida M. Cullen. Reprinted by permission of Harper & Row, Publishers, Incorporated.

HOLT, RINEHART & WINSTON, INC. — "The Pasture," from *You Come Too* by Robert Frost, copyright 1923, 1928, 1930, 1939, by Holt, Rinehart and Winston, Inc., copyright renewed 1951, copyright © 1956, © 1958 by Robert Frost. Reprinted by permission of Holt, Rinehart & Winston, Inc.

HOUGHTON MIFFLIN COMPANY — "Golden Rod," from *Little Folk Lyrics* by Frank Dempster Sherman.

J. B. LIPPINCOTT COMPANY — "The Reason for the Pelican," from *The Reason for the Pelican* by John Ciardi, copyright 1955 by the Curtis Publishing Company, reprinted by permission of J. B. Lippincott Company; "Blow the Stars Home," from *Poems for Children* by Eleanor Farjeon, copyright 1926, 1954, by Eleanor Farjeon. Reprinted by permission of J. B. Lippincott Company.

LITTLE, BROWN & COMPANY -- "Eletelephony," from *Tirra Lirra* by Laura E. Richards, copyright 1932 by Laura E. Richards; "Song of the Train," from *Far and Few* by David McCord, copyright 1952 by David McCord. Reprinted by permission of Little, Brown and Company.

THE MACMILLAN COMPANY — "Skyscrapers," from *Pointed People* by Rachel Field, copyright 1924, 1930 by The Macmillan Company; "The Moon's the North Wind's Cooky," from *Collected Poems* by Vachel Lindsay, copyright 1914 by The Macmillan Co., renewed 1942 by Elizabeth C. Lindsay; "White Fields," from *Collected Poems* by James Stephens, copyright 1915 by The Macmillan Company, renewed 1943 by James Stephens; "Sea Fever," from *Collected Poems* by John Masefield, copyright 1912 by The Macmillan Company, renewed 1940 by John Masefield. Reprinted by permission of The Macmillan Company.

MACMILLAN & COMPANY, LTD. — "White Fields," from *Collected Poems* by James Stephens. Reprinted by permission of Mrs. Iris Wise, the Macmillan Company of Canada, Ltd., and Macmillan Company, Ltd. of London, England.

McCLELLAND & STEWART, LIMITED — "A Vagabond Song," and "Winter Streams," from *Bliss Carman's Poems*. Reprinted by permission of McClelland and Stewart, Limited.

McGRAW-HILL BOOK COMPANY — "Little Fox Lost," and "Christmas Eve Legend," from *The Little Whistler* by Frances Frost, copyright 1949 by McGraw-Hill, Inc. Reprinted by permission of the publishers.

METHUEN & CO., LTD. — "The Happy Hedgehog," from *The Flattered Flying Fish* by Dr. E. V. Rieu. Reprinted by permission of Methuen & Company, Limited, London.

HAROLD OBER ASSOCIATES, INC. — "Blow the Stars Home," from *Eleanor Farjeon's Poems for Children*. Reprinted by permission of Harold Ober Associates, Inc., copyright 1926 by Eleanor Farjeon, copyright renewed 1954.

OXFORD UNIVERSITY PRESS — "The Tickle Rhyme," from *The Tale of the Monster Horse*, by Ian Serraillier. Reprinted by permission of Oxford University Press, London.

LAURENCE POLLINGER, LTD. — "The Pasture," from *The Complete Poems of Robert Frost*. Reprinted by permission of Laurence Pollinger, Limited, Authors' Agents.

G. P. PUTNAM'S SONS — "In the Summer," from *All Together* by Dorothy Aldis, copyright 1925, 1926, 1927, 1928, 1934, 1939, 1952, by Dorothy Aldis. Reprinted by permission of G. P. Putnam's Sons.

RANDOM HOUSE, INC. — "Where Are You Now?" from *All Aboard*, by Mary Britton Miller, copyright © 1958 by Pantheon Books, Inc. Reprinted by permission of Pantheon Books, a Division of Random House, Inc.

THE SOCIETY OF AUTHORS — "Some One," by Walter de la Mare, reprinted by permission of the Literary Trustees of Walter de la Mare and the Society of Authors as their representatives; and "Sea Fever," by John Masefield, by permission of the Society of Authors and John Masefield, O.M.

CHARLES SCRIBNER'S SONS — "Ducks' Ditty," from *The Wind in the Willows* by Kenneth Grahame, copyright 1908 by Charles Scribner's Sons, reprinted by permission of the publishers; and "Japanese Lullaby," from *Collected Poems of Eugene Field*, copyright 1910 by Charles Scribner's Sons.

A. P. WATT & SON — "Seal Lullaby," from *The Jungle Book* by Rudyard Kipling, reprinted by permission of Mrs. George Bambridge, copyright owner, the Macmillan Company of Canada, Ltd., and by Messrs. Macmillan & Co., Ltd., London.

THE WORLD'S WORK (1913) LTD. — "What is Brown?" from *Hailstones and Halibut Bones* by Mary O'Neill, reprinted by permission of The World's Work (1913) Ltd.

A careful effort has been made to trace the ownership of poems included in this anthology, in order to secure permission to reprint copyright material and to make full acknowledgment of their use. If any error of omission has occurred, it is purely inadvertent and will be corrected in subsequent editions, provided written notification is made to the publisher, Grosset & Dunlap, 51 Madison Avenue, New York, N. Y. 10010.

Read me a Poem